VFR Flight Rules

France

Daniel CASANOVA

CÉPADUÈS-ÉDITIONS
111, rue Nicolas-Vauquelin
31100 Toulouse – France
Téléphone : (de France) 05 61 40 57 36 – Fax : 05 61 41 79 89
(de l'étranger) + 33 5 61 40 57 36 – Fax : + 33 5 61 41 79 89
http://www.cepadues.com
e-mail: cepadues@cepadues.com

CHEZ LE MÊME ÉDITEUR

Dans la collection SFACT (Service de la Formation Aéronautique et du Contrôle Technique)

Manuel du pilote d'avion .... SFACT
Manuel du pilote – Vol à voile .... SFACT
Manuel du pilote – ULM .... SFACT
Pilotage des montgolfières .... SFACT

Série « Formation Pilote »

Réglementation aérienne .... Casanova D., Vacher P., Carme P.
Avionique de la navigation aérienne .... Combes M.
Propulseurs aéronautiques .... Lepourry P., Ciryci R.
Technique du vol .... Plays Y.
Instruments de bord .... du Puy de Goyne Th., Roumens A., Lepourry P.
Météorologie .... Renaudin M.
Cellules et circuits associés .... Ripoll J.-C.
Navigation et pratique de la radionavigation .... Sicre J.-L.
Bases d'électricité avion – Protection contre les incendies .... Valentin M.

Autres ouvrages

Le vol à voile à la Montagne Noire .... Alby R.
Le Guide du pilote : les Alpes et le Massif central .... Barrier R.
Regards sur l'Aviation civile – Histoire d'une Administration .... Brimeur D. et al.
La Météorologie du vol à voile .... Bradbury T.
Facteurs humains en aéronautique .... Campbell R.-D., Bagshaw M.
La Réglementation du pilote privé avion .... Casanova D.
Dictionnaire des sports aériens ultralégers (F-A / A-F) .... Dalla-Costa R.
Le Premier tour de France en planeur .... Floriot M.
Histoire du vol à voile français .... Jouhaud A. et R.
Dictionnaire de l'aéronautique – Du français vers l'allemand et l'anglais .... Krafft J.-H.
Dictionnaire technique de l'aéronautique (A-F / F-A) .... Lambert R.
Le Guide du pilote : les Pyrénées .... Mathon A.
La Légende des Guppy .... Méchain D.
Manuel de radiotéléphonie en langue anglaise – QRRI .... Montraisin J.-P.
Technique d'utilisation de l'hélicoptère – « T.U. Hélico » .... du Puy de Goyne Th., Koska M.
Découverte du pilotage avion .... du Puy de Goyne Th.
Théorie élémentaire de l'hélicoptère – versions française, anglaise et espagnole .... Raletz R.
Manuel de radiotéléphonie pour navigants professionnels (QRI), Tome I – 2e édition ...... Rengade Y.
Manuel de radiotéléphonie pour navigants professionnels (QRI), Tome II ...... Rengade Y., Roves G.
Manuel d'anglais parlé du pilote de ligne .... Rengade Y.
Manuel de vocabulaire anglais du pilote de ligne .... Roves G.
Guide de l'instructeur vol à voile .... SEFA
Guide pratique du pilote remorqueur .... SEFA
Guide des examens en vol PP/IFR .... Jury des examens – SFACT
Guide des épreuves pratiques de secourisme aéronautique (CSS) .... Jury des examens – SFACT
600 questions pour l'examen théorique de pilote privé avion .... Collectif

Logiciels

QCM du pilote privé (PC – 3,5") .... Nony O., Trébuchet F.
ISINAV – Logiciel d'entraînement à l'apprentissage des instruments de radionavigation VFR .... SEEE

Dépôt légal : mars 1998   N° éditeur : 467

SUMMARY

INTRODUCTION

CHAPTER ONE: FRENCH AIRSPACE

1. Airspace classification 7
2. Flight information regions. Lower airspace (FIR) 8
3. Flight information upper airspace (UIR) 8
4. Airspace restrictions and danger areas 8
5. French aviation territorial organisation 8
5. Aeronautical information 10

CHAPTER TWO: INTERCEPTION PROCEDURES

CHAPTER THREE: RULES OF THE AIR

1. Definitions 17
2. General rules 17
3. Priority 18
4. Minimum overflight heights 18
5. VFR flight plans 19
6. Fuel reserve 20

CHAPTER FOUR: VFR RULES

1. VFR flight 21
2. VFR weather minima 21
3. VFR in controlled airspace 22
4. VFR cruising levels 23
5. Preferential utilization of low altitude airspace 23

CHAPTER FIVE: AIR TRAFFIC SERVICES

1. Radar 25
2. Flight information service 25
3. Aerodrome 26
4. General provisions for aerodrome 28
4. Radiocommunications 30

CHAPTER SIX: SPECIFIC PROCEDURES

1. Procedure to cross the borders of metropolitan France 33
2. VFR diversion and transit routes within restricted or danger areas
   when operating under VFR (day) 37
3. Night VFR flight rules 37
4. Flight over the sea (maritime) 38

Introduction

This hand book is written for pilots holding a private licence who want to overfly or land in France. It tries to cover all the different aspects of VFR flight and regulations. It tries to help foreign pilots in their dealings with French ATC authorities.

The autor thanks his first readers Yves Rengade and David Edwards for their friendly remarks.

CHAPTER ONE

French airspace

1. AIRSPACE CLASSIFICATION

Class A, C, D, E and G are implemented in France.

AIRSPACE CLASS	AUTHORIZED FLIGHT	CONTROL SERVICE	FLIGHT DATA SERVICE	ALERT SERVICE	RADIO CONTACT MANDATORY	SUBJECT TO CLEARANCE	TYPE OF FLIGHT
A	IFR	spacing IFR/IFR	yes	yes	yes	yes	controlled
C	IFR & VFR	spacing IFR/IFR IFR/VFR traffic info VFR/VFR	yes	yes	yes	yes IFR & VFR	controlled
D	IFR & VFR	spacing IFR/IFR traffic info IFR/VFR VFR/IFR	yes	yes	yes	yes IFR & VFR	controlled
E	IFR & VFR	spacing IFR/IFR	yes VFR on request	yes	IFR yes VFR no	IFR yes VFR no	IFR controlled VFR not
G	IFR & VFR		yes on request	yes	IFR yes VFR no	no IFR & VFR	not controlled

2. FLIGHT INFORMATION REGIONS.
LOWER AIRSPACE (FIR).

FIR above metropolitan France are classified G from the surface to FL 195 excluding control regions and zones, specialized regions and zones.

LTA (Lower Traffic Area) situated between the highest levels FL 115 or 900 m ASFC and FL 195 is classified D, except TMA, AWY, CTR, specialized control areas and zones, restricted, dangerous and prohibited zones. LTA is classified E above the open sea (12 Nm from the French coasts).

TMA and S/TMA are classified D or E, except Genève TMA which are class C.

CTR and S/CTR are classified D or E, except Paris, Villacoubley and Jersey (at night) which are class A.

AWY are classified E from the lower limit to the higher of the following two levels: FL 115 or 3000 ft ASFC; D from this last level to FL 195. The portions of AWY located within a TMA/CTA also have this latter classification.

3. FLIGHT INFORMATION UPPER AIRSPACE (UIR).

VFR flights are prohibited in UTA (from FL 195 to FL 660) classified A.

4. AIRSPACE RESTRICTIONS AND DANGER AREAS

These areas are managed by the french AMC (Airspace Management Cell). There are prohibited (P), restricted (R), danger (D) areas and temporary segregated areas (TSA). TSA managed by the French AMC are published each day in Airspaces Users Publications (AUP).

There are also specific areas (R or D) for: parachute jumping, Aerobatics and model aircraft flying activities. National parks and nature reserves must be overflown at a minimum level (200, 300, 500 or 1 000 m).

In the absence of activities in some areas, users can be informed by administrators and possible additional orders be transmitted by an automatic answering service operating on the frequency on which users normally have to contact administrators.

5. FRENCH AVIATION TERRITORIAL ORGANISATION

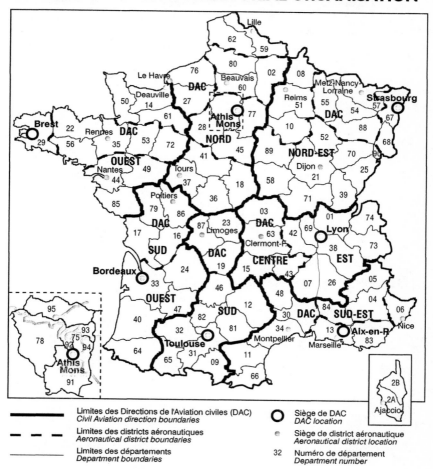

▬▬▬▬	Limites des Directions de l'Aviation civiles (DAC) *Civil Aviation direction boundaries*	◯ Siège de DAC *DAC location*
▬ ▬ ▬ ▬	Limites des districts aéronautiques *Aeronautical district boundaries*	⊜ Siège de district aéronautique *Aeronautical district location*
────	Limites des départements *Department boundaries*	32 Numéro de département *Department number*

France is divided in six civil aviation directions (DAC) who manage the general aviation and all the aerodromes. The DAC are divided in aeronautical districts.

DAC OUEST located in Brest with the districts of Rennes, Deauville and Nantes.

DAC NORD located in Athis-Mons (near Paris) with the districts of Le Havre, Lille, Beauvais and Tours.

DAC NORD EST located in Strasbourg with the districts of Reims, Metz-Nancy-Lorraine and Dijon.

DAC CENTRE EST located in Lyon with the district of Clermond-Ferrand.

DAC SUD EST located in Aix en Provence with the districts of Montpellier, Marseille, Nice and Ajaccio.

DAC SUD located in Toulouse with the district of Limoges.

DAC SUD OUEST located in Bordeaux with the district of Poitiers.

Foreign pilots may obtain all aeronautical administrative informations in DAC or districts.

6. AERONAUTICAL INFORMATION

6.1. FLIGHT PLAN ON FRENCH TERRITORY

MINITEL server: 3614 CODE PLN

6.2. NOTAM ON FRENCH TERRITORY

MINITEL server: 3614 CODE NOTAM

6.3. SUPPLEMENTARY INFORMATION

To obtain supplementary information and file directly a flight plan, pilots should apply to :
- AIS office or AIS reporting office of the aerodrome where they are;
- Regional flight assistance information office (BRIA in French).

BRIA	PHONE NUMBER	FAX
1. LILLE	03 20 16 19 65/66	03 20 87 51 14
2. BALE MULHOUSE	03 89 90 26 15/12	03 89 90 26 19
3. LYON	04 72 22 56 76/77/78	04 72 23 80 67
4. MARSEILLE	04 42 31 15 65 / 04 42 14 22 90	04 42 31 15 69
5. NICE	04 93 21 38 18	04 92 29 41 32
6. AJACCIO	04 95 22 61 85	04 95 23 59 69
7. TOULOUSE	05 62 74 65 31/32	05 62 74 65 33
8. BORDEAUX	05 57 92 82 71/72	05 57 92 83 34
9. NANTES	02 40 84 84 75 / 02 40 84 80 45	02 40 84 30 39
10. LE BOURGET	01 48 62 53 07	01 48 62 72 07

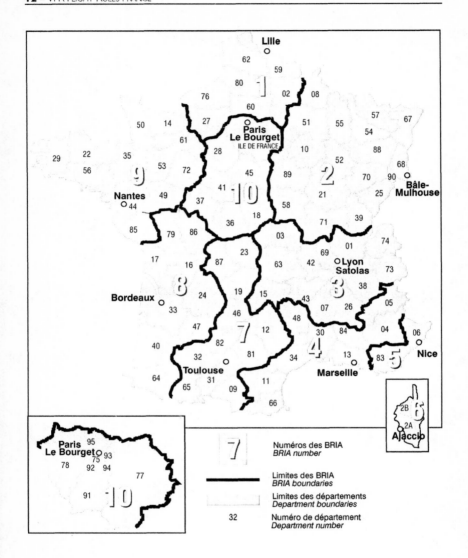

Chapter two

Interception procedures

Signals initiated by intercepting aircraft and responses by intercepted aircraft	
INTERCEPTING aircraft signals	**Meaning**
Day or night: Rocking aircraft and flashing navigational lights at irregular intervals (and landing lights in the case of a helicopter) from a position slightly above and a head of, and normally to the left of the intercepted aircraft (or to the right if the intercepted aircraft is a helicopter) and, after acknowledgement, a slow level tur, normally to the left (or to the right in the case of a helicopter) on the desired heading.	You have been intercepted. Follow me.
Note 1: meteorological conditions or terrain may require the intercepting aircraft to reverse the positions and direction of turn given above.	
Note 2: if the intercepted aircraft is not able to keep pace with the intercepting aircraft the latter is expected to fly a series of race-track patterns and to rock the aircraft each time it passes the intercepted aircraft.	
INTERCEPTED aircraft responses	**Meaning**
Day or night: Rocking aircraft, flashing navigational lights at irregular intervals and following.	Understood, will comply.

INTERCEPTING aircraft signals	Meaning
Day or night: An abrupt break away manoeuvre from intercepting aircraft consisting of a climbing turn of 90 ° or more without crossing the line of flight of the intercepted aircraft.	You may proceed

INTERCEPTED aircraft responses	Meaning
Day or night: Rocking the aircraft.	Understood, will comply.

INTERCEPTING aircraft signals	Meaning
Day or night: Lowering landing gear (if fitted), showing steady landing lights and overflight runway in use or, if the intercepted aircraft is a helicopter, overflying the helicopter landing area. In case of helicopters, the intercepting helicopter makes a landing approach, coming to hover near to the landing area.	Land at this aerodrome

INTERCEPTED aircraft responses	Meaning
Day or night: Lowering landing gear (if fitted), showing steady landing lights and following the intercepting aircraft and, if, after overflying the runway in use or helicopter landing area, landing is considered safe, proceeding to land.	Understood, will comply.

INTERCEPTED aircraft signals	Meaning
Day or night: Raising landing gear (if fitted) and flashing landing lights while passing over runway in use or helicopter landing area at a height exceeding 300 m (1 000 ft) but not exceeding 600 m (2 000 ft) (in the case of a helicopter, at a height exceeding 50 m (170 ft) but not exceeding 100 m (330 ft) above th aerodrome level, and continuing to circle runway in use or helicopter landing area. If unable to flash landing lights, flash any other lights available.	Aerodrome you have designated is inadequate

INTERCEPTING aircraft signals	Meaning
Day or night: If it is desired that the intercepted aircraft follow the intercepting aircraft to an alternate aerodrome, the intercepting aircraft raises its landing gear (if fitted) and uses the series 1 signals prescribed for intercepting aircraft.	Understood, follow me
Day or night: If it is decided to release the intercepting aircraft, the intercepting aircraft uses the series 2 signals prescribed for intercepting aircraft.	Understood, you may proceed
INTERCEPTED aircraft signals	**Meaning**
Day or night: Regular switching on and off of available lights but in such a manner as to be distinct from flashing lights.	Cannot comply.
INTERCEPTING aircraft responses	**Meaning**
Day or night: Use the series 2 signals prescribed for intercepting aircraft.	Understood.
INTERCEPTED aircraft signals	**Meaning**
Day or night: Irregular flashing of all available lights.	In distress.
INTERCEPTING aircraft signals	**Meaning**
Day or night: Use the series 2 signals prescribed for the intercepting aircraft.	Understood.

CHAPTER THREE

Rules
of the air

French air traffic regulations conform with recommended standards and practices specified in ICAO Annexes 2 and 11, excepting the following provisions.

I. DEFINITIONS

There are three sorts of aerodrome in France. Controlled Airport via a TWR service, non controlled Airport and AFIS agency. Airport Flight Information Service is an air traffic agency in charge of the aerodrome flight information service and alerting service for the aerodrome service of a non controlled aerodrome.

2. GENERAL RULES

French regulationsadd to the pilot's authority in ICAO Annex 2 two points:

— the pilot in command is responsible for application of clearances given by an air traffic service. Such clearances can in no way be used by the pilot in command to fail to comply with any regulation.

— a(ny) crew member must cease to perform his duties as soon as he feels any physical trouble or fatigue.

3. PRIORITY

As in Annex 2 French regulations also, an aircraft must give way to another on its right priority. There are specific rules:

– In the case of aircraft flying in the proximity of the side of a mountain and parallel to it, priority is given to the aircraft with the slope to its right and only the other aircraft shall deviate from its flight path.

– Engine powered aircraft shall give way to aircraft towing other aircraft or objets, or formations consisting of more than two aircraft.

4. MINIMUM OVERFLIGHT HEIGHTS

4.1. GENERAL RULE

Except for the take-off and landing and related procedures, aircraft must fly at levels that are above or equal to the highest of the following levels:

– the minimum height which would permit the aircraft, when flying over towns and other built up areas, to land clear and without danger to persons or property in event of engine failure;

– minimum heights relative to the overflying of towns and other built-up areas asprescribed by the arrêté (decree) of 1957:

OVERFLYING	SINGLE PISTON ENGINE	MULTI ENGINE OR TURBO
Factory, Industrial building, Hospital, Motorway	300 m (1 000 ft)	1 000 m (3 000 ft)
Built-up areas < 1,2 Km Open air gatherings	500 m (1 500 ft)	1 000 m (3 000 ft)
1,2 < built-up areas < 3,6 Km Gatherings of more than 10 000 persons	1 000 m (3 000 ft)	1 000 m (3 000 ft)
Built-up areas > 3,6 Km except Paris. Gatherings of more than 100 000 persons	1 500 m (4 500 ft)	1 500 m (4 500 ft)

– minimum height according to VFR or IFR rules.

4.2. MINIMUM VFR LEVEL

No VFR flight may be undertaken (except for take-off and landing procedure):

– over cencentrations of population, towns or other built-up areas, or over gatherings of people and animals in open areas, at less than 1 000 ft above the highest obstacle located within a radius of 600 m of the aircraft;

– over an artificial obstacle (person, vehicle, ship, house...), at a height of less than 500 ft above ground or water and at a distance of less than 150 m from it.

5. VFR FLIGHT PLANS

A flight plan may be filed in VFR before flight. During flight when it is necessary to obtain clearance to cross class D controlled airspaces, join circuit at a controlled aerodrome or obtain a special VFR clearance, pilots transmit flight data to an ATS unit, this unit considers this transmission as are "abbreviated" flight plan.

A VFR flight plan is mandatory for:

– VFR flights crossing the borders of metropolitan France (see chapter 6);

– Night VFR flights (see chapter 6);

– VFR flights over maritime regions (see chapter 6). France considers a region maritime when the distance from the coast exceeds the lower of the following two distances:
  • the distance required to ensure that a landing can be made on land in the event of engine failure;
  • a distance equivalent to 15 times the aircraft's altitude.

The closure of the abbreviated flight plan shall be made by radio on leaving the controlled airspace or on the apron leaving the frequency.

The closure of flight plan shall be made by radio communication exchange if the arrival aerodrome is equipped with an ATS unit. When no ATS unit exists on the arrival aerodrome, the closure of flight plan must be made:

– as soon as possible after landing by telephone to the nearest ATS unit or Flight Information Centre;

– by radio, a few minutes before landing, with an ATS unit.

6. FUEL RESERVE

The pilot have to carry the fuel quantity to the destination according to the wind plus 20 minutes for day flight and 45 minutes for night flight.

CHAPTER FOUR

VFR
rules

I. VFR FLIGHT

VFR flight is permitted only in lower airspace up to and includice FL 195.
VFR flights are controlled in class D airspaces and in aerodrome traffic zones.
There are specific regulations concerning flights accross the channel and over
the Mediterranian. An aircraft flying VFR must be equipped with radiocom-
munication and radionavigation instruments when it loses sight of the ground
or the sea.

2. VFR WEATHER MINIMA

VMC conditions consider two values:
– FL 100;
– "S" surface.

"S" corresponds to the higher of these two levels:
– 900 m (3 000 ft) above mean sea level, or
– 300 m (1 000 ft) above the ground.

Above "S" surface, an aircraft performing a VFR flight must be set a two way
communication with the service concerned and then remain in contact. Non
radio aircraft must remain in sight of the surface at all times. There are non
radio routes avoiding class D areas.

2.1. VMC CONDITIONS

Visibility:
- Class C, D and E: 8 km above FL 100, 5 Kms below it;
- Class G: 8 km above FL 100, 5 Kms between FL 100 and "S" surface, and the higher of the two values, 1 500 m or 30 seconds' flight, below "S" surface.

Cloud distances:
- Class C, D and E: 1 500 m horizontally, 300 m vertically;
- Class G: 150 m horizontally, 300 m vertically above "S" and out of clouds below it.

Speed limitations:
- 250 kt below FL 100.

2.2. SPECIAL VFR WEATHER MINIMA IN CTR

Ceiling: 450 m

Visibility: 5 km

Under these values the VFR pilot may request a SVFR clearance. In France there is no overall national standard. Each aerodrome with a control zone has its own SVFR minima but never less than: surface visibility 1 500 m, ceiling 300 m.

3. VFR IN CONTROLLED AIRSPACE

LTA from FL 115 up to FL 195 is in class D airspace, where ATC clearance and radio contact are mandatory. The same procedure applies in AWY, TMA and CTR in class D.

In airspaces AWY, TMA and CTR in class E there is no requirement for ATC clearance or radio contact. However, although radio contact is not mandatory it is recommended.

In class G radio contact is recommended when the flight is for more than one hour or 200 km.

To enter in Class C (Lyon TMA, Nice and Toulouse shortly) the aircraft have to carry a transpondor A + C and to request a clearance on TMA information frequency. A VFR pilot can receive clearence with IFR level, heading and so on. But the pilot may refuse the clearance to maintain VMC conditions. The controller gives him an other clearence.

4. VFR CRUISING LEVELS

VFR flights are required to comply with the semi-circular cruising level rule when operating above "S" surface.

Magnetic track 000°-179°: FL 35, 55, 75, 95, 115, 135, 155, 175 and 195;

Magnetic track 180°- 359°: FL 45, 65, 85, 105, 125, 145, 165 and 185.

Below "S" altitude is free. In controlled airspaces the semi-circular cruising level rule is required for VFR flights operating above Transition Altitude. In France the national standard for transition altitude is 5 000 ft. Between Transition altitude and "S" VFR Flights comply:

Magnetic track 000°-179°: 3 500 feet above Mean Sea Level;

Magnetic track 180°- 359°: 4 500 feet above Mean Sea Level.

5. PREFERENTIAL UTILIZATION OF LOW ALTITUDE AIRSPACE

Military low level operations are mostly carried out Monday to Friday between Sunrise plus 30 minutes and Sunset minus 30 minutes. These operations are conducted at very high speed below 1 500 ft. So pilots operating under VFR are recommended to:

– conduct their flights at a cruising level at or 1 500 ft above the surface in accordance with meteorological conditions and airspace restrictions;

– make essential flights only during the "Datex" military exercices (as announced in NOTAM).

CHAPTER FIVE

Air traffic services

French ATS provide Control, Information and Alert services in accordance with ICAO Annex 11. But in France Alerting service is provided to all aircraft with or without flight plan and any aircraft that is known or assumed to be subject to an unlawful interference. Air traffic services requirements for information are not included in French regulations.

1. RADAR

French ATS provide radar assistance, radar surveillance and radar control for the Information, Alert and Control Services.

Transponders are mandatory :
– Within class C mode A + C
– Within class D mode A or S (A + C recommended)
– Above FL 120 mode A or S

Aircraft equipped with mode C should squawk Code 7 000 (VFR code) unless otherwise directed by ATC. Aircraft with Mode A only, squawk only as directed by ATC.

2. FLIGHT INFORMATION SERVICE

Flight information services are provide by ACC and Approach centres. It is recommended to contact ACC (Brest, Paris, Reims, Bordeaux, Aix en Provence) above FL115 and Approach below. In France ACC are also FIC (Flight Information Centers) and some Approach centers have FIS (Flight Information Sector, see the map). In case of radio failure in airspace where radio is mandatory. The pilot shall:

– after receiving clearance to join the airspace (class D for exemple), comply with the last clearance given and proceed standard; don't enter the airspace before receiving clearance.

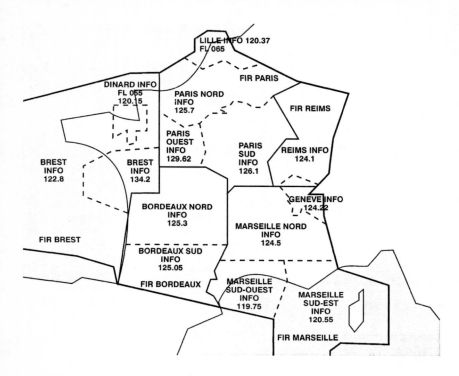

French flight information sector provides information on meteorology, infrastructure and know traffic. Radar vectoring suggestions are only provided on pilot request.

3. AERODROME

3.1. DEFINITIONS

There are three sorts of aerodrome in France:
- Controlled aerodromes, with tower (TWR) service only during the working hours of the control office;
- Non-controlled aerodromes, where the pilot himself provides radio procedure (but generally in French);
- AFIS. Aerodrome Flight Information Service provide only Informations and Alert services. The «officer» on frequency don't give any clearance. Only during the working hours of the control office.

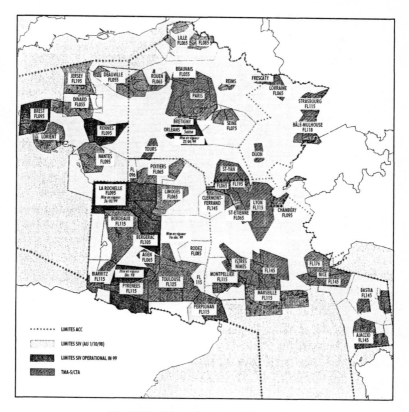

FLIGHT INFORMATION SECTOR

3.2. PROVISIONS RELATING TO PARAMETERS

Pilots are deemed to be informed of the parameters when the first five of those listed below are known.

– runway in use,
– surface wind speed and direction, and variations,
– ground visibility,
– QFE,
– QNH,

- ceiling,
- air temperature,
- transition level when needed,
- exact time.

4. GENERAL PROVISIONS FOR AERODROME

4.1. POSITIONS

The characteristic positions of a typical surface traffic pattern and a typical aerodrome traffic circuit are:

1	apron
2	holding point
3	lined up
4	initial climb
5	cross wind
6	down wind abeam mid runway
6b	down wind
7	base leg entry point (outside the circuit)
7b	base leg
8	last turn
9	long final (at circuit height)
9b	final
10	runway vacated

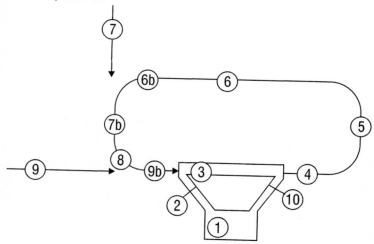

4.2. TYPES OF CIRCUITS

A variety of different taxiing circuits and aerodrome circuits may be established on an aerodrome for use by different types of aircraft (gliders, helicopters, airplanes, ...). Pilots have to follow them.

4.3. STANDARD CIRCUITS

There are no stardard circuits in France stricly specified, but a as general rule according to the aircraft's performance:

- fly the down wind leg at 1 000 ft above aerodrome surface when permitted by the cloud height;

- make all turns leftwards;

- when the pilot pulls up to go around, he has to manoeuver to avoid the other aircraft in the circuit.

There are particular instructions on some aerodromes, such as right hand turns onto a runway, specific altitude, recommendations to avoid some areas (hospital, town, ..), pilots are oblized to comply.

4.4. CIRCUIT JOINING PROCEDURES

4.4.1. Controlled aerodrome

Tower gives clearance and informs pilots. Any aircraft must obtain clearance before they:

- join the circuit (in down wind leg, base leg or final approach) and move on the ground;

- enter a runway;

- take off or land.

4.4.2. On AFIS

AFIS agency informs pilots about traffic and parameters. When it is possible an aircraft may join the circuit directly in final approach or base leg.

4.4.3. Non controlled aerodrome

After he has been informed of the parameters or assessed them, the pilot notes the position of any other aircraft in the circuit and he shall join the traffic at the starting point of the down wind leg. Pilot ensures a visual separation from any other aircraft.

Nota: the best way to know parameters and traffic is to overfly the signal area and the circuit (minimum 500 ft above in VFR) and join after the starting point of the down wind leg.

5. RADIOCOMMUNICATIONS

5.1. FREQUENCIES

Pilots shall transmit position reports:
– on arrival, before joining the circuit;
– on departure, before leaving the apron;

On controlled aerodromes and AFIS, the pilot operates on the frequency assigned; on non-controlled aerodromes with no assigned frequency, the pilot uses 123,5 MHz.

5.2. PROCEDURES

Pilots have to transmit standard position reports to the controlled aerodrome and at any other position following request from the control tower. On AFIS or via self information procedure (non-controlled aerodrome) at these following positions:

Arrival:
– before joining the circuit;
– on the down wind leg;
– on the base leg;
– on the final leg;
– when the runway is vacated;
– on the apron.

Departure:
- on the apron, before moving;
- at the holding point;
- on the runway ready to take-off;
- when leaving the aerodrome circuit.

5.3. RADIO FAILURE

5.3.1. Controlled aerodrome or AFIS with radio mandatory

Should a radio failure occur, pilots shall:
- on departure: not take-off;
- on arrival after receiving clearance to join the circuit, comply with the last clearance given and proceed standard circuit to land. Look out for visual signals from the tower;
- on arrival before receiving any clearance not join the circuit unless an emergency occurs. In this case fly above the circuit directly over the tower and look out for visual signals.

5.3.2. Non controlled aerodrome or AFIS where radio is not mandatory

Should a radio failure occur, pilots shall:
- on departure: not take-off before warning the AFIS centre;
- on arrival: fly vertically over the aerodrome at an altitude above the circuit and then join the circuit on down wing leg and following standard procedure.

Example: Visual landing chart of Amiens Glisy (LFAY).

This is an AFIS aerodrome frequency 123.4 in French only.

For example – Not in use

ATTERRISSAGE A VUE
Visual landing

Ouvert à la CAP
Public Air Traffic

01 AMIENS GLISY LFAY
95 04 27

ALT en pieds
ALT AD : 197 (7 hPa)

LAT : 49 52 24 N
LONG : 002 23 23 E
DÉC 3°W (90)

APP : NIL
TWR : NIL
AFIS : AMIENS Information 123.4 (HR). En l'absence AFIS A/A en HR seulement.

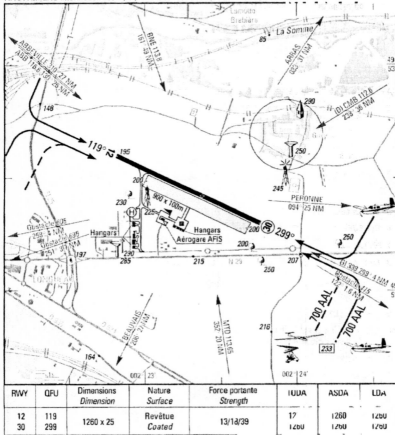

RWY	QFU	Dimensions Dimension	Nature Surface	Force portante Strength	TODA	ASDA	LDA
12	119	1260 x 25	Revêtue Coated	13/18/39	12	1260	1260
30	299				1260	1260	1260

Aides lumineuses BI RWY 12/30
mise en oeuvre du balisage
possible par télécommande.

Lighting aids : LIL RWY 12/30
ground lighting can be
operated by remote control.

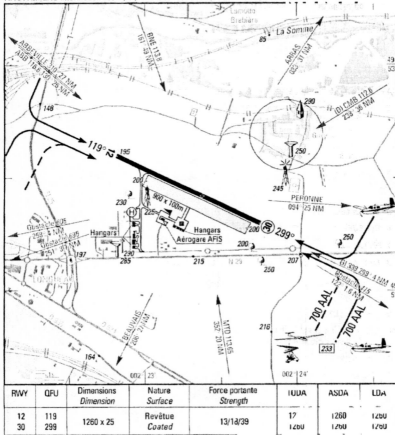

FRANCE

CORRECTIONS: Nouvelle présentation

©SIA

CHAPTER SIX

Specific procedures

1. PROCEDURE TO CROSS THE BORDERS OF METROPOLITAN FRANCE

1.1. FLIGHT PLAN

Pilots must file a flight plan to cross land or sea territorial borders of France. This flight plan must be submitted at least 30 minutes before the estimated off block time. The border crossing point must be entered in item 15 of the flight plan and the estimated time to reach this point in item 18 after indicator EET/. Remember that flight plan can only close after arrival at the aerodrome of destination or the alternate.

1.2. RADIO CONTACT

When pilots entry or leave French Airspace, they must contact a French air traffic control unit. If it is impossible to establish first with the Flight Information Center or Flight Information Sector concerned they may preferably contact the border aerodromes concerned:

AJACCIO/CAMPO DELL'ORO	LFKJ
BALE/MULHOUSE	LFSB
BASTIA/PORETTA	LFKB
BIARRITZ/BAYONNE/ANGLET	LFBZ
CALAIS/DUNKERQUE	LFAC
CHAMBERY/AIX LES BAINS	LFLB
LILLE/LESQUIN	LFQQ
NICE/COTE D'AZUR	LFMN

PERPIGNAN/RIVESALTES   LFMP
STRASBOURG/ENTZHEIM   LFST

If the pilot cannot make this contact, after landing he must contact the police and customs services to have a link with ACC.

The mandatory report message shall include information:
– aircraft registration;
– aerodrome of departure and destination;
– "border crossed" indication;
– position, altitude, time.

1.3. CONDITIONS FOR USE CUSTOMS, IMMIGRATION AND HEALTH SERVICES

To enter France pilots have to file a flight plan at a customs airport. For all aerodromes, operating periods and hours are set out in NOTAM.

AJACCIO CAMPO DELL'ORO	LIMOGES BELLEGARDE
BASTIA PORETTA	LYON BRON
BEAUVAIS TILLÉ	LYON SATOLAS
BÉZIERS VIAS	MARSEILLE PROVENCE
BIARRITZ BAYONNE ANGLET	METZ FRESCATY
BORDEAUX MÉRIGNAC	MONTPELLIER MÉDITERRANÉE
BREST GUIPAVAS	NANCY ESSEY
CALVI SAINTE CATHERINE	NANTES ATLANTIQUE
CANNES MANDELIEU	NICE CÔTE D'AZUR
CHAMBÉRY AIX LES BAINS	NIMES GARONS
CHÂTEAUROUX DÉOLS	PAU PYRÉNÉES
CHERBOURG MAUPERTUS	PERPIGNAN RIVESALTES
CLERMONT FERRAND AULNAT	POITIERS BIARD
COLMAR HOUSSEN	RENNES SAINT-JACQUES
DINARD PLEURTUIT ST MALO	RODEZ MARCILLAC
GRENOBLE SAINT GEOIRS	SAINT ÉTIENNE BOUTHÉON
HYÈRES LE PALYVESTRE	SAINT NAZAIRE MONTOIR
LANNION	STRASBOURG ENTZHEIM
LA ROCHELLE LALEU	TARBES OSSUN LOURDES
LE HAVRE OCTEVILLE	TOULOUSE BLAGNAC
LE TOUQUET PARIS PLAGE	TOURS ST SYMPHORIEN
LILLE LESQUIN	VICHY CHARMEIL

I.4. INTERNATIONAL GENERAL AVIATION "INTRA-SHENGEN" FLIGHTS

The order of the 20 April 1998, concerning the opening of aerodromes to international air traffic and applicable with effect from the 1st June 1998, introduces special provisions for the benefit of general aviation flights carried out between the European territory of the French Republic and the other States Implementing the Convention which puts into effect the Schengen Agreement of the 14 June 1985.*

These flights which remain international flights and for that reason continue to be subject in particular to the obligation to file a Flight Plan, may involve their departure from or arrival at French aerodromes, in accordance with the following provisions :

• aerodromes open to international traffic, referred to in the AIP France (see 1.3) : outside the published hours of opening to the international air traffic, these aerodromes are accessible to them, subject to prior information from the Prefect of the Department in which is situated the aerodrome concerned, with prior 24-hours notification, by facsimile to the number given in the appendix;

• aerodromes not open to international traffic, including heliports and landing grounds approved for use by powered ultra-light aircraft,, these aerodromes are accessible to them, provided that the use for which they are intended be observed and subject to prior information from the Prefect of the Department (Préfet du département) in which is situated the aerodrome concerned, with prier 48 -hours notification, by facsimile to the number given in the appendix.

N° Dépt	Département	N° Fax	N° Dépt	Département	N° Fax
01	Ain	04 74 32 30 55	49	Maine-et-Loire	02 41 81 82 27
02	Aisne	03 23 20 69 58			02 41 71 28 82
03	Allier	04 70 48 30 77			02 41 67 19 88
04	Alpes de Haute-Provence	04 92 32 26 91	50	Manche	02 98 37 34 94
05	Hautes-Alpes	04 92 40 49 62			02 40 84 80 39
06	Alpes-Maritimes	04 92 29 41 32	51	Marne	03 26 21 08 40
07	Ardeche	04 92 53 79 49			03 26 65 29 05
08	Ardennes	03 24 58 35 21	52	Haute-Marne	03 25 32 02 26
09	Ariège	05 61 02 74 82	53	Mayenne	02 43 56 72 85
			54	Meurthe-et-Moselle	03 83 30 52 34

*As of the lst June 1998, the States implementing this Convention will be : Germany, Austria, Belgium, Spain, France, Italy, Luxembourg, Holland and Portugal.

10	Aube	03 25 73 77 16
11	Aude	04 68 72 32 98
12	Aveyron	05 65 68 25 67
13	Bouches-du-Rhône	04 91 15 64 35
14	Calvados	02 31 30 65 52
		02 31 30 64 90
15	Cantal	04 71 64 88 01
16	Charente	05 45 97 62 62
		05 45 97 61 94
17	Charente-Maritime	05 46 27 43 39
18	Cher	02 48 70 41 41
19	Corrèze	05 55 26 82 02
2A	Corse-du-Sud	04 95 29 00 36
2A	Haute-Corse	04 95 34 06 82
21	Côte-d'Or	03 80 44 69 21
22	Côtes-d'Armor	02 96 62 43 85
23	Creuse	05 55 52 48 61
24	Dordogne	05 53 08 88 27
25	Doubs	03 81 83 21 82
26	Drome	04 75 42 87 55
27	Eure	02 32 78 28 09
28	Eure-et-Loire	02 37 27 70 44
29	Finistère	02 98 33 17 79
30	Gard	04 77 41 72 22
31	Haute-Garonne	05 61 33 40 79
		05 61 33 36 81
32	Gers	05 62 61 43 74
33	Gironde	05 56 90 60 67
34	Hérault	04 67 02 25 79
35	Ille-et-Vilaine	02 99 02 11 69
36	Indre	02 54 29 47 05
37	Indre-et-Loire	02 47 64 04 05
38	Isère	04 76 51 34 88
39	Jura	03 84 60 08 92
40	Landes	05 58 06 59 69
41	Loir-et-Cher	02 54 81 54 03
42	Loire	04 77 41 72 22
43	Haute-Loire	04 71 09 78 40
44	Loire-Atlantique	02 40 35 30 97
45	Loiret	02 38 81 40 22
46	Lot	05 65 23 11 90
47	Lot-et-Garonne	05 53 68 09 36
48	Lozère	04 66 49 67 22

55	Meuse	03 29 79 64 49
56	Morbihan	02 97 54 59 45
57	Moselle	03 87 34 85 32
58	Nièvre	03 86 36 12 54
59	Nord	03 20 30 52 52
60	Oise	03 44 45 39 00
61	Orne	02 33 80 61 65
62	Pas-de-Calais	03 21 21 23 06
63	Puy-de-Dôme	04 73 98 61 01
64	Pyrénées-Atlantiques	04 68 34 68 51
65	Hautes-Pyrénées	05 62 51 20 10
66	Pyrénées-Orientales	04 68 34 68 51
67	Bas-Rhin	03 88 59 93 99
68	Haut-Rhin	03 89 24 70 15
		03 89 24 71 18
69	Rhône	04 78 60 15 46
70	Haute-Saône	03 84 76 49 60
71	Saône-et-Loire	03 85 21 81 01
72	Sarthe	02 43 28 24 09
73	Savoie	04 79 75 50 83
74	Haute-Savoie	04 50 33 64 00
75	Préfecture de Paris	01 48 87 47 83
76	Seine-Maritime	02 35 98 10 50
77	Seine-et-Marne	01 64 71 78 04
		01 64 71 76 22
78	Yvelines	01 39 49 78 72
79	Deux-Sèvres	05 49 08 69 04
80	Somme	03 12 92 13 98
81	Tarn	05 63 49 50 60
82	Tarn-et-Garonne	05 63 93 33 79
83	Var	04 94 18 82 87
84	Vaucluse	04 90 85 03 00
85	Vendée	02 51 36 70 27
86	Vienne	05 49 88 25 34
87	Haute-Vienne	05 55 77 58 13
88	Vosges	03 29 82 42 15
89	Yonne	03 86 49 53 55
90	Territoire-de-Belfort	03 84 57 15 36
91	Essonne	01 69 91 90 34
92	Hauts-de-Seine	01 47 25 12 44
93	Seine-Saint-Denis	01 41 60 60 71
94	Val-de-Marne	01 49 56 64 17
95	Val-d'Oise	01 34 25 20 32

2. VFR DIVERSION AND TRANSIT ROUTES WITHIN RESTRICTED OR DANGER AREAS WHEN OPERATING UNDER VFR (DAY)

In France there are experimental VFR transit routes within restricted airspaces. Three types of flight routes are specified:

A- Recommended (Open for all aircraft, radio contact is not mandatory);

B- Compulsory with radio contact

C - Compulsory without radio contact

Authorization for use A, B or C routes shall be obtained from TWR or APP. Flight routes outside restricted zones are drawn to facilitate the link between different zones.

3. NIGHT VFR FLIGHT RULES

Night VFR is permitted in France. Official night extends from SS + 30 min to SR – 30 min. The limitations are :

– the pilot must have an IFR licence or a Night VFR licence ;

– the aircraft must be equipped for night flight ;

– a flight plan is not mandatory for a flight between two airfields depending of the same approach service and for a flight start on the day continuing after sunset if the pilot is in contact with the ATC service ;

– VFR night flight is prohibited in airways ;

– aerodrome of departure and landing must be equipped (lights and control unit) ;

– ceiling :
  • Local flight : 300 meters above obstacle in 8 km radius
  • Travel : 450 meters above obstacle in 8 km radius and 600 meters if the obstacle is over 1500 meters ;

– visibility :
  • Local flight : ≥ 5 km.
  • Travel : maintain the ground or the seain sight with the base of cloud height ≥ 450 meters above the cruise level expected and with no dangerous meteorological phenomena ;

– Transponder mode A + C with altitude report.

4. FLIGHT OVER THE SEA (MARITIME)

To flight over the sea life jacket are mandatory at more 50 miles. For single engine at more 100 miles and 200 miles for multi-engines the aircraft have to carry:

– emergency location transmitter;

– a dinghy with complete life equipment.

4.1. WESTERN MEDITERRANEAN

General aviation aircraft are authorized to fly over the western mediterranean sea under VFR rules when following the routes and in compliance with procedures. This is mainly for Search and Rescue purpose but will also assist ATC.

4.1.1. Flight routes

Flight routes start from France via Nice, Cannes and Saint Tropez, from Corsica via Ajaccio, Bastia and Calvi and from the Balearic islands from Mahon. (sea the map). There are mandatory points to enter French airspace from Italy: POULP from Alghero (Sardinia), FIR limit to the island of Elba, TORTU to Genova. MERLU is a mandatory point between Cannes and Saint Tropez to Corsican aerodromes.

4.1.2. Procedures

Pilots shall, when flying maritime routes:

– file a flight plane;

– make flight position reports;

– Nice air traffic centre provide radio communication from the continental coast to MERLU point and Corsican centre (Ajaccio or Bastia) from this point to the island;

– maintain radio communication.

4.1.3. Flight altitude

Pilots choose altitude at any time to allow direct VHF communication, according with the semi-circular rule.

4.2. CHANNEL

The following procedures complete the border crossing regulations.

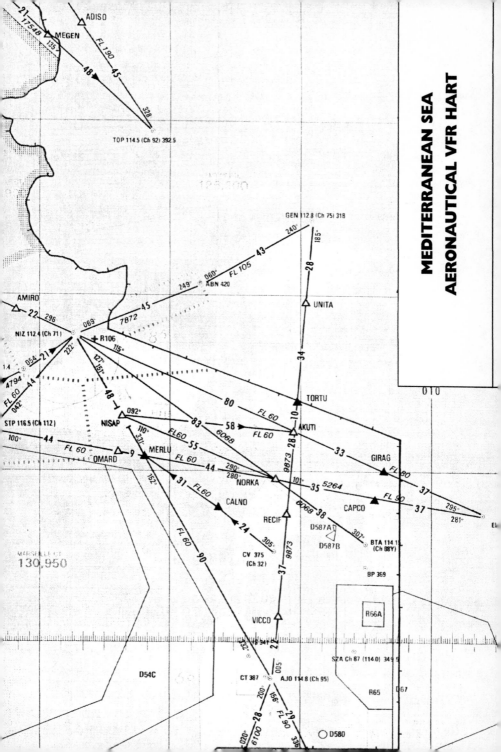

MEDITERRANEAN SEA
AERONAUTICAL VFR HART

4.2.1. FLIGHT ROUTES

Cross channel flights between London FIR, Paris FIR and Brest FIR must follow the routes specified in the flight plan. When is filing this flight plan, pilots are to ensure that well defined significant points/features, at which the aircraft expected to cross the United Kingdom and French coastlines, are included in item 15 of the flight plan form. This is mainly for Search and Rescue purposes but will also assist ATC.

4.2.2. Procedures to be followed by pilots

– file a flight plan;

– choose altitude at any time to allow direct VHF communication with an ATC unit, in accordance with the semi-circular rule;

– maintain radio communication;

– transmit a position report message when crossing the FIR boundary and the French coast [this message is transmitted first to the appropriate FIC (Paris, Brest) or preferably FIS (Brest, Calais, Cherbourg, Deauville, Dinard, Landivisiau, Lannion, Le Havre, Le Touquet, Lille, Morlaix, Saint Brieux)];

– position report message to include:
  • Aircraft identification;
  • Aerodrome of departure and destination;
  • position and time;
  • altitude;
  • ETA above the next position report point.

– transponder mode A or C is recommended.

4.2.3. London air traffic control information centre

The LATCC provides a flight information service to pilots flying in the open FIR. The service for the area is available on frequency 124.6 with call sign "London Information" (information service only). Alert service is provide by Royal Air Force, also in LATCC, 24 hours nationwide emergency cover both civil and military.

4.3. CHANNEL ISLANDS

Within Brest FIR, between France and the Channel Islands, aircraft must enter Jersey CTR via the entry points (sea the map). The procedures to be followed by pilots are the same as for cross Channel flights except these following points:
— pilots shall report position to Brest Information or Dinard FIS when crossing the French coast and when entering Jersey CTR. Jersey APP when crossing the French coast and arriving from East;
— Transponder equipment mode A is mandatory for VFR flights within the Channel Islands CTR and CTA.

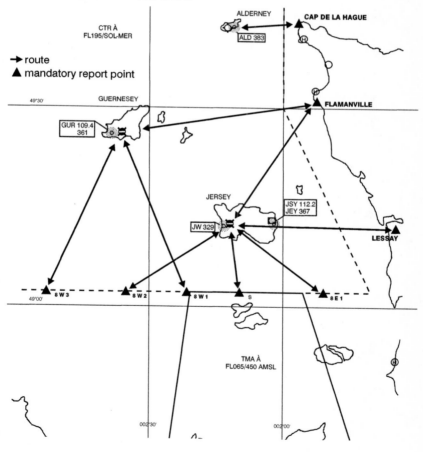

MESSAGES
111, rue Nicolas-Vauquelin
31100 Toulouse

Juillet 1998